The Humungous Doug Horley Songbook

THE Humungous

DOUG HORLEY

Songbook

CHILDREN'S MINISTRY

Eastbourne

Music arranged and set by Simon Fenner

Cover design by Pinnacle Creative

Printed in the United Kingdom by Halstan & Co. Ltd, Amersham, Bucks for
KINGSWAY COMMUNICATIONS LTD
Lottbridge Drove, Eastbourne, East Sussex, BN23 6NT, UK.
childrensministry@kingsway.co.uk

Well, here you have it. A collection of just about all the songs I've written over the years since my very first family album called 'Jesus is the Boss', right up to the 'Okey Dokey' album.

My heart is simply to see children and grown ups touch the heart of God through having fun as they sing to him. Funky songs, action songs, quiet songs, adult songs and songs that I don't quite know what category they fit into! They're all here. And it's been so exciting to see these songs travel around the world and be used by children's workers right across the globe. I hope you have as much fun singing them as I did writing them. And I hope they bring you closer to God's heart.

What an amazing God we have and what a privilege it is to worship him. And isn't it incredible that it's ok to have fun in the process.

May you bring a huge smile to God's face!

Doug

24-7

(Not Just When The Sun Is Shining)

Doug Horley

Not just when the sun is shin - ing,
Not just when my bank is smil - ing,

not just when my plans are fly - ing.
not just when the clouds are part - ing.

Not just when I'm feel - ing, I'm feel-ing fine.
Not just when it's fun and life is cool.

On those days when life goes pear - shaped,
On those days the car's back fir - ing,

on those days can't get my hair straight.
on those days the toast - er's dy - ing.

On those days I want to run and hide.
On those days my keys just run and hide.

Help me turn to You, ooh, my Lord. 'cause

Taken from
Lovely Jubbly
KMCD2384

(I Will Praise Your Name For Ever)

Doug Horley

Taken from
Lovely Jubbly
KMCD2384

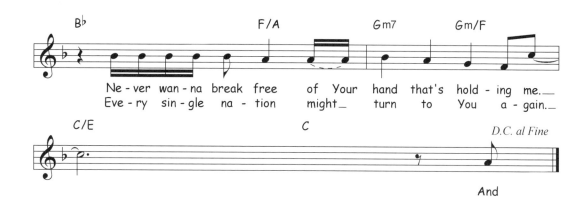

Bb F/A Gm7 Gm/F

Ne - ver wan - na break free of Your hand that's hold - ing me.__
Eve - ry sin - gle na - tion might__ turn to You a - gain.__

C/E C

D.C. al Fine

And

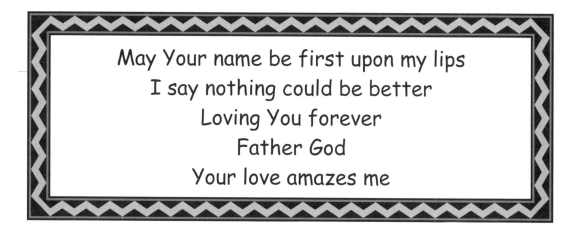

May Your name be first upon my lips
I say nothing could be better
Loving You forever
Father God
Your love amazes me

All Right Now

(We Have Joy, We Live Right)

Original words by A. Fraser & P. Rodgers
Alteration of lyrics by Noel Richards

Taken from
Jesus Is The Boss
KMCD827

A-oh, A-oh Let's Get Funky!

(Now is the time)

Doug Horley
Rap: Efrem Buckle

Taken from
Okey Dokey
CHMCD034

Rap 1:

It's time to move if you feel the groove
There's no time to lose now squash those blues and
Celebrate cos you're feeling great
Now don't you waste this treble and bass and
Tell your friends that we're back again
To set a new trend a mix and a blend of
Hip hop and funk and pure praise
Get on your feet be funky your way

Rap 2:

Come on
All the girls in the house get up
Don't you get stuck it's time to get funky
All the boys in the house get up
Don't you get stuck it's time to get funky
Mums and dads in the house get up
Don't you get stuck it's time to get funky
Everybody in the house get up
Don't you get stuck it's time that everybody...

Bish, Bash, Splish, Splash

(Faith Is Being Sure Of What You Hope For)

Doug Horley

Taken from
Fandabidozzie
CHMCD023

Waa, waa, waa.   Who knows what God will...   Bish, bash, splish, splash.

D.C. al Fine

Wick, wack, smick, smack.   Waa, waa, waa.   Who knows what God will do.

Stand firm in the faith
Be men of courage
Be strong
Do everything in love

Be On Your Guard

Doug Horley

Be on your guard. stand firm in the faith, be men of cour-age, be strong. Be on your guard, stand firm in the faith, be men of cour-age be strong. Do eve-ry-thing in love, eve-ry-thing in love. Do eve-ry-thing in love, eve-ry-thing in love. Do eve-ry-thing in love. Be on your eve-ry-thing in love.

Taken from
Fandabidozzie
CHMCD023

Blessed Be The Name Of The Lord

Clinton Utterbach

CMDH05

Taken from
Jesus Is The Boss
KMCD827

Bounce

(Oh, Won't You Let Me See)

Doug Horley

Oh, won't You let me see more of Your mys - ter - y;
I know You'll al - ways be more than a friend to me;

I can't ex - plain how You love me like You do.
You hold me close and You'll ne - ver let me go.

Now I have re - a - lised my mind was hyp - no - tised
It's such a mys - ter - y, why You should care for me.

by this cruel world, I was lost but now I'm found.
I can't ex - plain why You love me like You do.

So let it go, now ba - by, let it

flow now, praise from your heart; let it start. Let it

go, now ba - by, let it flow now, praise from your heart, let it start.

Taken from
Lovely Jubbly
KMCD2384

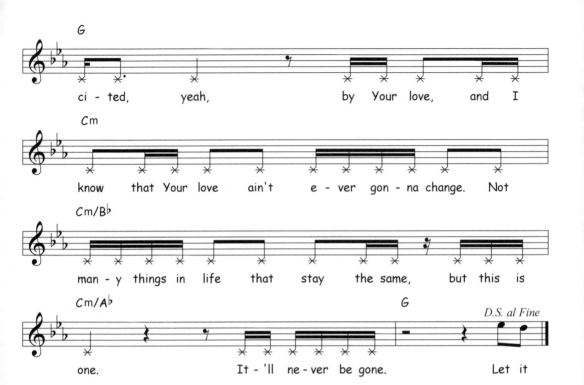

ci - ted,   yeah,   by Your love,   and I

know   that Your love   ain't   e - ver gon - na change.   Not

man - y things in   life   that   stay   the same,   but this is

one.   It - 'll ne - ver be gone.   Let it

D.S. al Fine

I know You'll always be
More than a friend to me;
You hold me close and You'll never let me go.
It's such a mystery,
Why You should care for me.
I can't explain why You love me like You do.

Can Sheep Speak Danish?

Doug Horley

Taken from
Lovely Jubbly
KMCD2384

true,   true,   true.   God loves you, it's true, not a lie, for - gives

you, it's true, not a lie. Ac - cepts you, it's true, not a lie. Yes, it's

true,   true,   true.   Can   true.

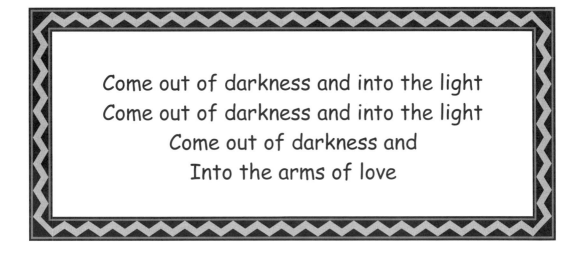

Come out of darkness and into the light
Come out of darkness and into the light
Come out of darkness and
Into the arms of love

Come Out Of Darkness

Doug Horley & Noel Richards

Taken from
We Want To See Jesus Lifted High/King Of Heaven
KMCD2438 & On Eagles' Wings KMCD2296

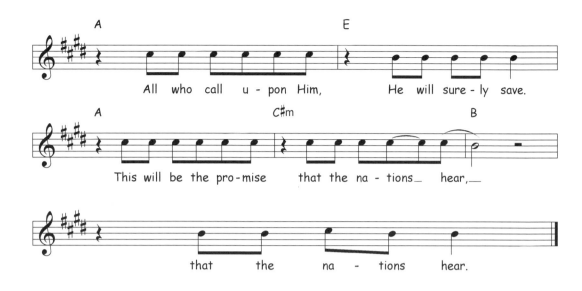

All who call u-pon Him, He will sure-ly save.

This will be the pro-mise that the na-tions— hear,—

that the na - tions hear.

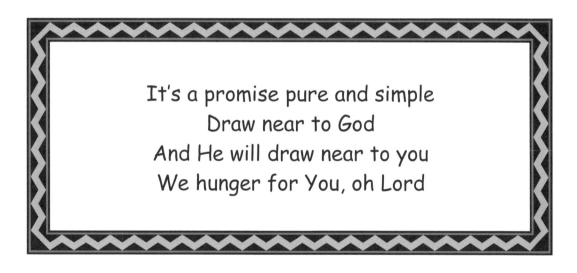

It's a promise pure and simple
Draw near to God
And He will draw near to you
We hunger for You, oh Lord

Come To The Father

Doug Horley

Taken from
We Want To See Jesus Lifted High/ King Of Heaven
KMCD2438 & On Eagles' Wings KMCD2296

Do Not Worry

Doug Horley

Do not wor - ry,___ oh, oh.___ Do not wor - ry,___ oh, oh.___ Do not wor - ry,___ oh, oh___ 'bout a - ny-thing. Do not a - ny-thing. Do not wor - ry___ a - bout a - ny - thing___ but pray and ask God for ev' - ry - thing you need and when you pray, oh, oh,___ al-ways give thanks and the peace of God___ will keep your mind___ in Je - sus. Do - not a - ny-thing. Does wor-ry e - ver stop bad things hap-pen-ing? No! And it won't help

Taken from
We Want To See Jesus Lifted High/King Of Heaven
KMCD2438

Do Not Fear

Doug Horley

Taken from
Fandabidozzie
CHMCD023

Every Day That I Live

(You Are My God)

Doug & Belinda Horley, & Steve Whitehouse

You are my God, how I love You. You are my friend, how I need You. You are my strength, You are my hope, You are my song.

Eve-ry day that I live, I will hon-our You. Eve-ry dream that You give, I will cling to. Eve-ry day I will try to make You smile. Noth-ing ev-er for You is im-pos-si-ble. All the prob-lems we face,

Eve-ry hurt, eve-ry pain, I will give to You. In my sun-shine and rain, I will wor-ship You. I will hold noth-ing back from You, my King. All my doubts and my fears are much small-er now. I don't face them a-lone,

Taken from
Lovely Jubbly
KMCD2384

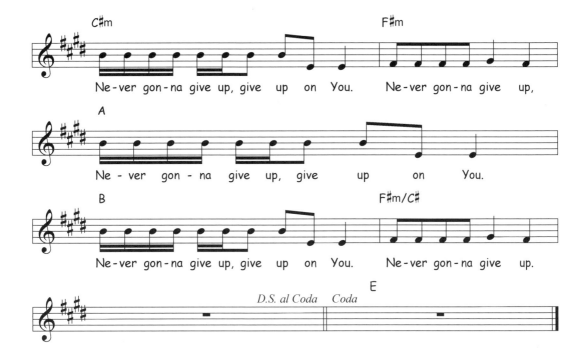

C#m

Ne - ver gon - na give up, give up on You.

F#m

Ne - ver gon - na give up,

A

Ne - ver gon - na give up, give up on You.

B

Ne - ver gon - na give up, give up on You.

F#m/C#

Ne - ver gon - na give up.

D.S. al Coda   Coda

E

Faith As Small As A Mustard Seed

Doug Horley

Faith as small as a mus-tard seed___ will move moun-tains, move moun-tains. Faith as small as a mus-tard seed___ will move moun-tains by the pow-er of God. God. Be-lieve what Je-sus said was true. Be-lieve He meant it just for you. Wait and see what God will do, as you pray.___ As you pray.___ God. Do, da, do, da, do, da, do,___ do, da, do, da, do, da, moun-tains. Do, da, do, da, do, da, do,___ do, da, do, da, do, da, mus-tard.

Taken from
Whoopah Wahey
KMCD2217

Fandabidozzie

16

(He's The Gaffa, He's The Guv'nor)

Doug Horley, Steve Whitehouse & Pete Bignall

(Capo 1 Em)

Fm (Em)

He's the gaf - fa, He's the guv' - nor, He's the big, big cheese. Head hon - cho, head hon - cho. He's the chief of our be - lief, He is the ma - ker of our teeth, no

B♭m (Am)

great - er, cre - a - tor. El Su - pre - mo,__ Nu - mer - o - u - no.

Fm (Em) ... **%B♭m (Am)**

Hea - ven's num - ber one.__ Es-pi - ri - tu San - to

C (B)

come in power we cry to__ You.__ He is

Fm (Em) ... **E♭ (D)**

fan - da - bi - do - zzie, fan - da - bi - do - zzie. He's the God__ of

Fm (Em)

eve - ry - thing. Fan - da - bi - do - zzie, fan - da - bi - do - zzie,

16

Taken from
Fandabidozzie
CHMCD023

Father God I Wonder

Ian Smale

Taken from
Jesus Is The Boss
KMCD827

Glory and honour to You we bring.
Beautiful Saviour Your praise we sing.
Heaven bows down and worships Your name.
God of creation we praise.

Glory And Honour

Doug Horley

CMDH05

Taken from
Okey Dokey
CHMCD034

God Is For You

(Let These Words Sink Into Your Heart)

Doug Horley & Vanessa Freeman

Taken from
We Want To See Jesus Lifted High/King Of Heaven
KMCD2438

God Loves Me

Pete Bignall, Peter Tye & Steve Whitehouse

Taken from
Lovely Jubbly
KMCD2384

Hands, Hands, Fingers, Thumbs

Doug Horley

Taken from
We Want To See Jesus Lifted High/King Of Heaven
KMCD2438

Hark The Herald Angels Sing

Words by Charles Wesley (1707-1788)
Music arranged by Doug Horley

Hark, the he-rald an-gels sing. Hark, the he-rald an-gels sing.

Hark the he-rald an-gels sing glo-ry to the new born King. Peace on earth and mer-cy mild,

God and sin-ners re-con-ciled. Joy-ful all the na-tions rise,

join the tri-umph of the skies. With the an-ge-lic host pro-claim,

Christ is born in Beth-le-hem. Hail the hea-ven born Prince of Peace,

hail the Son of right-eous-ness. Light and life to all He brings,

ri-sen with heal-ing in His wings. Mild He lays His glo-ry by,

Taken from
We Want To See Jesus Lifted High/King Of Heaven
KMCD2438

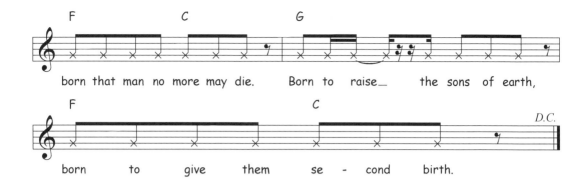

born that man no more may die. Born to raise_ the sons of earth,

born to give them se - cond birth.

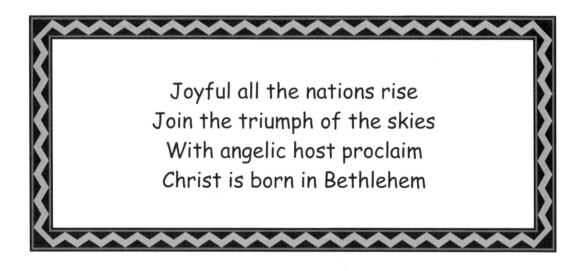

Joyful all the nations rise
Join the triumph of the skies
With angelic host proclaim
Christ is born in Bethlehem

Have We Made Our God Too Small?

Doug Horley

Taken from
We Want To See Jesus Lifted High/King Of Heaven
KMCD2438

CMDH05

C#m
awed by the marks of God___ all a-round me. Yet I'm

B
hum - bled eve - ry day by my un - be - liev - ing ways. I

A   B   *D.S. al Coda Coda*   B   E
real - ly, real - ly want it to change.___ Have we you and I.

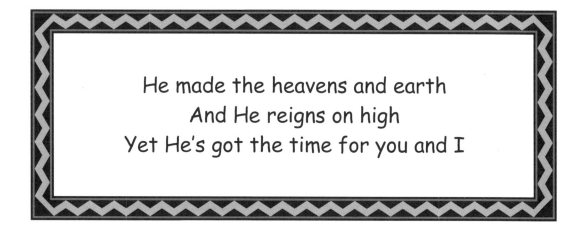

He made the heavens and earth
And He reigns on high
Yet He's got the time for you and I

Heavenly Dad

Doug Horley

Hea-ven-ly Dad, You make my heart so glad.

You make me, make me want to sing.___ It's just so good, just so

good to know You love___ me.___ Hea-ven-ly Dad,

You make my heart so glad.___ You make me, make me want to sing.___

It's just so good, just so good to know You love___

___ me.___ And in Your___ arms___ I will___ stay___ what could be bet -

ter for - e - ver___ to walk with___ You___ and

talk with___ You?___ Oh___ I will al - ways love You.___

Taken from
Jesus Is The Boss
KMCD827

It's just so good to know You love me.
And in Your arms I will stay
What could be better
For ever to walk with You and talk with You.
Oh I will always love You.

Help Me Be Your Eyes Lord Jesus

25

(I Got You Lord)

Doug Horley

(Capo 4 D)

Taken from
Fandabidozzie
CHMCD023

Hey Diddle Diddle

Doug Horley

Taken from
Okey Dokey
CHMCD034

be a-fraid, this is a joy-ful__ day. Stuff the e-ne-my,

God has set me free now.

Coda

Hey did - dle, did - dle won't you dance in the mid-dle?

Hey did - dle, did - dle won't you dance in the mid-dle?

Hey did-dle, did-dle won't you dance in the mid-dle to-night?____

Hey, Hey!

27

Doug Horley

Taken from
Fandabidozzie
CHMCD023

Higher, Higher

(Cast Your Burdens)

28

Isaac Balinda

Taken from
Jesus Is The Boss
KMCD827

Hold On To The Promises Of God

Doug Horley

CMDH05

Taken from
We Want To See Jesus Lifted High/King Of Heaven
KMCD2438

lieve what I say___ 'cos it's meant___ to___ be."___ You got - ta

2. Now Abraham believed what God said was true
   But in case he was wrong he had plan number two,
   And through his servant he got himself a son.
   He thought at last the promise had come
   But God said, "This is your plan not mine,
   I'll do it my way and in my time."

3. God said to Abraham, "Look up in the sky
   Count all the stars way, way up high.
   That's the size of family I'll give you
   If you obey what I say in all that you do.
   That's the good news, but now here's a surprise,
   The bad news is, you've gotta be circumcised!"

4. So Isaac was born and A'bram was proud,
   But a voice from on high
   Came through clear and loud.
   "This boy will be a sacrifice."
   A'bram said, "Hey that's not very nice."
   But by now he knew it really paid to obey.
   He said to Isaac, "We're going out for the day."

5. Tied hand and foot, on his back Isaac lay
   As his Dad raised the knife he knew this was not his day!
   But with seconds to spare God stepped in time,
   Isaac said, "Phew! Well you cut that a bit fine."
   God said to Abraham, "You've past the last test,
   You really have proved, you're the best of the best."

I Believe

Doug Horley

Taken from
Okey Dokey
CHMCD034

I Can Walk, I Can Run

31

Doug Horley

Taken from
Okey Dokey
CHMCD034

I Love You

(God I Pray, Please Help Me)

Doug Horley
Rap: Efrem Buckle

God I pray,— please help— me— see the power of heaven— hold - ing me and ne - ver let - ting— go,— ne - ver let - ting go.— Ev' - ry day,— sur-round - ed— by a love e - ter - nal God— I know I'm safe in Your arms,— safe in Your arms.— I love You, I— love— You. Ev'-ry day— help me come a lit - tle clos - er. I love You, I— love— You. God of all— I wor - ship You. I love You.

Taken from
Okey Dokey
CHMCD034

Rap:

There's no where that compares to this place
In Your arms I'm safe
By Your grace I know my sins are erased
And I feel my heart ablaze
You take my hand
And give me all the strength to stand
And make me a brand new man
So I do, bare my heart to You
I tell You that it's true that I love You
I love You
Cos I know that...

I Stand Amazed

Doug Horley & Efrem Buckle

(Capo 3 G)

I, I stand a-mazed, by Your love, by Your grace, Lord Je-sus.

I, I stand a-mazed, by Your love, by Your grace.

Who would e-ver be-lieve it true,

the depth of love that flows out of You.

You hold my life in Your hand and how You whis-per

love so ten-der-ly. You know my sin and You know my shame.

I cause You grief and I cause You pain,

but still You choose from the heights of heav'n, to shout Your

Taken from
Fandabidozzie
CHMCD023

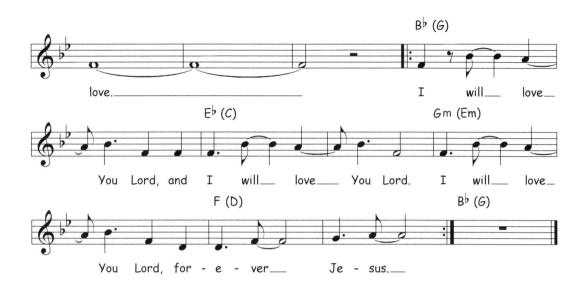

love._____ I will__ love__

You Lord, and I will__ love__ You Lord. I will__ love__

You Lord, for - e - ver__ Je - sus.__

Who would ever believe it true
The depth of love that flows out of You
You hold my life in Your hand
And how You whisper love so tenderly

I Wanna Be A Bloomin' Tree

34

(I Wanna Be A Tree That's Bearing Fruit)

Doug Horley

Taken from
We Want To See Jesus Lifted High/King Of Heaven
KMCD2438

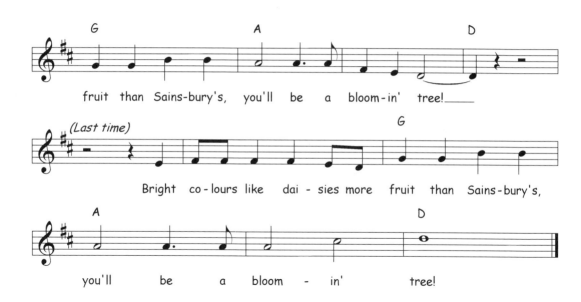

fruit than Sains-bury's, you'll be a bloom-in' tree!____

(Last time)

Bright co-lours like dai - sies more fruit than Sains-bury's,

you'll be a bloom - in' tree!

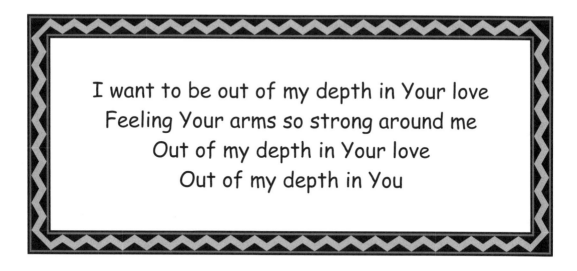

I want to be out of my depth in Your love
Feeling Your arms so strong around me
Out of my depth in Your love
Out of my depth in You

I Want To Be Out Of My Depth In Your Love

35

Doug & Belinda Horley, Noel Richards, Hayley Roberts & Penny Webb

I want to be out of my depth_ in Your love,___ feel - ing Your arms____ so strong____ a - round_ me.____ Out of my depth__ in Your love,____ out of my depth_ in____ You.____ Learn-ing to let_ You lead,_ put - ting all trust__ in You.____ Deep-er in - to____ Your arms,_ sur-round-ed by You. Things I have held__ so tight,____ made my se-cu - ri - ty,_____ give me the strength_

Taken from
We Want To See Jesus Lifted High/King Of Heaven
KMCD2438 & On Eagles' Wings KMCD2296

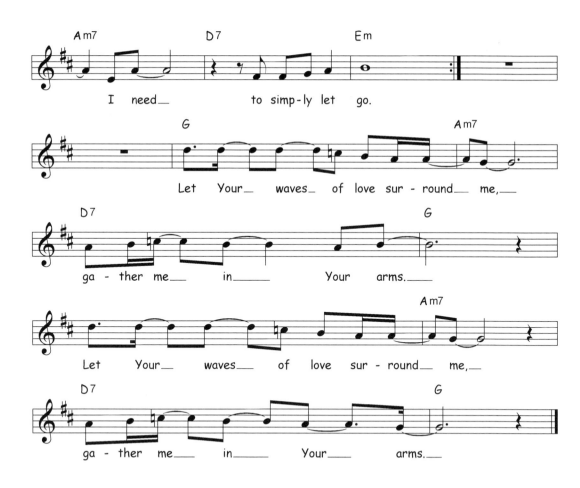

I Will Be Yours

(Keep Your Thoughts Pure)

36

Doug Horley

One! Keep your thoughts pure.
Two! Keep your mind pure.
Three! Keep your body holy.
1, 2, 3, Go!

You maybe see, hear, read stuff that has a great attraction
Whoopah, way-hey, yeah, but what's your reaction?
Watch what you're getting on your stereo or TV
Hitting something dodgy is so flip, flip, easy
Hey, what? Check this, so easy to get side tracked
Ev'ry body needs to keep their guard - up!
Don't stash no trash in your mind, resist it
'Cos once it's in you know it's hard to shift it.

(Capo 2 Em)

Keep your thoughts pure, keep your mind pure. Keep your bo-dy ho - ly.

Keep your thoughts pure, keep your mind pure. Aah.____

I, I will be Yours,____ for-e-ver - more,____ un-til the end_

of____ time.____

You gotta know, that there's nothing need ever rock ya.
The power of three in one is God and hey you know He's gotcha.
ONE, God'll love you no matter what may happen.
TWO, The Holy Spirit's here to guide every action.
THREE, The son of God is real you know He is no dream.
Ask Jesus to come and give your mind a spring clean.

There's a power word you have that Satan hates to hear.
Makes him shake, shake in his boots, shiver with cold fear.
You can shoot his hoop, leave him no where left to go.
This is the word, just say - No!

Taken from
Whoopah Wahey
KMCD2217

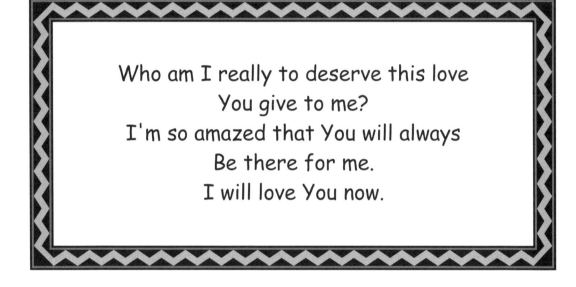

Who am I really to deserve this love
You give to me?
I'm so amazed that You will always
Be there for me.
I will love You now.

I Will Love You Now

37

(Whatever Life May Bring)

Doug Horley & Mark Read

What-e-ver life may bring,___ what moun-tains
What-e-ver tears may fall,___ when wor-ries

we must climb,___ the laugh-ter we might share,___ the times we
cloud my smile,___ I vowed we'd ne-ver part___ then si-lence

stop and stare. At beau-ty in Your eyes,___ the mo-ment
broke Your heart. Faith tried be-yond be-lief,___ but You were

of sur-prise.___ This is___ my prom-ise___ to You. And
there for me,___ Your grace___ is all that___ I need.

ah, when I think of all You___ sa-cri-ficed for___ me.___ And

ah, so hum-bled that it brings me to my knees. And I,

I will love___ You now,___ with all that's in-side of me. And for-

Taken from
Okey Dokey
CHMCD034

I Would Be Lost Without You

Doug Horley

Taken from
We Want To See Jesus Lifted High/King Of Heaven
KMCD2438

ea-si-ly we take for grant - ed love.__ Oh I wish it was-n't true.__

Do You know how much__ I__ count__

__ on You?__ Desp - erate - ly__ de - pend__ on You?__

Know it's true.____

I'm Forever In Your Love

39

Doug Horley

Taken from
Whoopah Wahey
KMCD2217

I'm Gonna Jump Up And Down

(Be Happy!)

40

Doug Horley

I'm gon-na jump up and down, gon-na spin right a-round, gon-na praise Your name__ for-e - ver. I'm gon-na shout out loud, gon-na deaf - en the crowd,__ gon - na send my praise to hea - ven.

1. I'm gon-na__ *2.* ven. *Fine*

I will run this race and I will ne-ver stop. I'll fol-low Je - sus till the day__ I drop. I can do all things through Christ who strength-ens me. When you've got such a lot,

D.S. al Fine

when you've got not a lot, what? Be hap - py!_____ I'm gon-na

Taken from
Lovely Jubbly
KMCD2384

I'm Gonna Build My House On Solid Rock

41

Doug Horley

Taken from
We Want To See Jesus Lifted High/King Of Heaven
KMCD2438

2. Jesus said, take my words, and put them into action
   Make these words He said, foundations in your life.
   Build with care or else, your house will surely tumble
   And it's not a clever trick, to own a heap of bricks.

3. Jesus said, take my words, and put them into action
   Make My words He said, foundations in your life
   And when the river comes, and crashes up against you
   You won't get washed away instead you'll cheer and say!

   Yes I built my house on solid rock
   Yes I built my house on solid rock
   And I won't wake up to a nasty shock
   To find nothing but a pile of rubble.

I'm Not Just Here To Use Up Air

42

Doug Horley & Mark Read

Taken from
Okey Dokey
CHMCD034

Is There A Plank In Your Eye?

43

Doug Horley

Is there a plank in your eye? Big e-nough to walk on, big e-nough to build a ship or may be start a bon-fire. Is there a plank stuck in your eye? Stuck, stuck, stuck. Is there a stuck. Don't point a fin-ger and say, Oy! You're do-ing it wrong when hey, hey. Your own life is far from O K. Don't point at the speck in your bro-ther's eye, when there's a

Taken from
Whoopah Wahey
KMCD2217

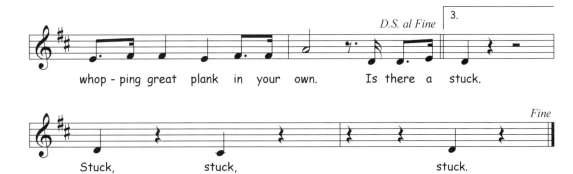

whop - ping great plank in your own. Is there a stuck.

Stuck, stuck, stuck.

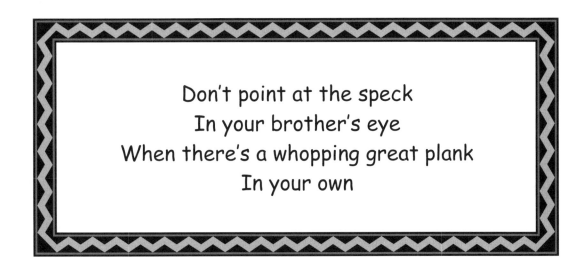

Don't point at the speck
In your brother's eye
When there's a whopping great plank
In your own

I've Got A Wobbly Tooth! 44

Doug Horley

Taken from
We Want To See Jesus Lifted High/King Of Heaven
KMCD2438 & On Eagles' Wings KMCD2296

Jesus Is The Boss

(The Gift Of God Is Eternal Life)

45

Doug Horley

The gift of God is e-ter-nal life through Je-sus Christ. The gift of God is e-ter-nal life through Je-sus Christ. The gift of God is e-ter-nal life through Je-sus Christ. Through Je-sus, Je-sus Christ. Je-sus is the boss of my life, He's the on-ly one can make it come right. Je-sus is the boss of my life. Je-sus is the boss.

I'm a friend of Jesus Christ
He's God's Son and He's alive.
I will trust in Him it's true
He's always there to see my through.
Sound of - Jesus,
Sound of - is Lord.
Sound of - Jesus,
Sound of - is Lord!

I said come on everybody and move your feet
The rhythm is hot it's a powerful beat.
The time is right to do some business
Get on your feet and be a witness,
To the Holy One
The King of kings, God's only Son
Jesus Christ, that's His name.
He died to take our sin and shame.

Taken from
Jesus Is The Boss
KMCD827

Jabulani Africa

46

(Jesus, Life And Hope To Heal Our Land)

Fini De Gersigny

Je - sus, life and hope to heal our land. Je - sus, reach - ing out with Your migh - ty hand. Sing for joy oh A - fri - ca, the Lord your God is ri - sen u - pon you. Sing for joy oh A - fri - ca the Lord your God is ri - sen u - pon you, now! Ja - bu - la - - ni, ja - bu -

Taken from
Whoopah Wahey
KMCD2217

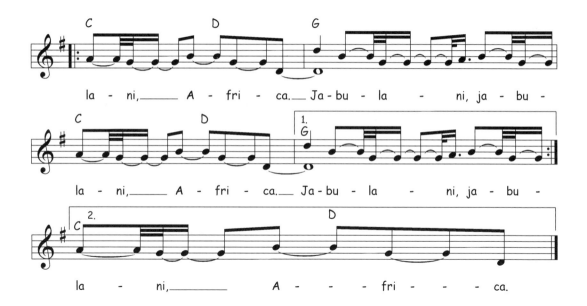

la - ni,_____ A - fri - ca.___ Ja-bu - la - ni, ja - bu -

la - ni,_____ A - fri - ca.___ Ja-bu - la - ni, ja - bu -

la - ni,_____ A - - - fri - - - ca.

Jesus, river of life to our thirsty land
Saviour, meeting our needs from Your mighty hand.
Sing for joy, oh Africa
The Lord your God is risen upon you.
Sing for joy, oh Africa
The Lord your God is risen upon you - Now!

Author Unknown

Taken from
Jesus Is The Boss
KMCD827

Jump Up

(Cast Your Worries To Him)

Doug Horley & Efrem Buckle

(Capo 4 Em)

Jump up, jump up. Put your hands high.

Sing out, sing out. Let your praise fly.

Shout out, shout out. Let your voice ring.

You know you can trust the King of kings. Jump

You know you can trust the King of kings.

Jump up, ev'-ry-bo-dy in the house now.

Sing out, ev'-ry-bo-dy in the house now.

Shout out, ev'-ry-bo-dy in the house.

You know you can trust the King of kings.

Taken from
Fandabidozzie
CHMCD023

I say Je-sus, you say Sav-iour. Je-sus, Sav-iour, Je-sus, Sav-iour.

I say Sav-iour, you say Je-sus. Sav-iour, Je-sus, Sav-iour, Je-sus.

G#m (Em)

Jump up, ev'-ry-bo-dy in the house now.

Sing out, ev'-ry-bo-dy in the house now.

Sing out, ev'-ry-bo-dy in the house.

1, 2, 3. (D)
F#   G#m (Em)

You know you can trust the King of kings.

4. (D)
F#   G#m (Em)

You know you can trust the King of kings. Jump up!

King Of Heaven

(There's A King Above The Heavens)

Doug Horley & Vanessa Freeman

49

Taken from
We Want To See Jesus Lifted High/King Of Heaven
KMCD2438 & On Eagles' Wings KMCD2296

King Of Love

50

Doug Horley

King of love, praise You. King of love, wor-ship You.

King of love, thank You. I'm trea - sure in___ Your___ eyes...

trea - sure in___ your___ eyes.___

I know my heart will love You for - e - ver.___

I know Your word, I'll al - ways___ be___ Your___ child.___

I know my soul is safe for e - ter - ni - ty, 'cos You hold___ me

close. In Your arms. In Your arms.

Taken from
Whoopah Wahey
KMCD2217

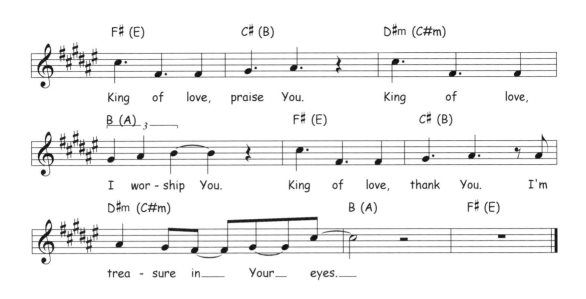

King of love, praise You. King of love,
I wor-ship You. King of love, thank You. I'm
trea-sure in__ Your__ eyes.__

I know my heart
Will love You forever
I know Your word
I'll always be Your child

Let It Out

(You Have Brought Joy To Me)

51

Doug Horley & Paul Butler

You have brought joy to me, I've felt the warmth of hea - ven's smile. You know my eve - ry breath, You're watch - ing o - ver me. You know my good and bad, ups and downs, my hopes and dreams.. Your eyes see eve - ry - thing and yet You still love me. And eve - ry day we will bring our wor-ship to You. Eve - ry day we will give our prai-ses to You. Eve - ry day we will

Taken from
Lovely Jubbly
KMCD2384

Let Your Fire Fall

52

(Lord You've Chosen Us To Be)

Doug Horley & Noel Richards

Lord You've cho-sen us to be car-ri-ers of Your

flame. Cho-sen us to be, war-ri-ors of light. Call-ing all the

na-tions to the bright-ness of Your dawn.

You, have touched with ho-ly fire those who bear Your

name. Now fill us with a love for the lost a-gain, as we stir to

ac-tion go be-fore us, send Your power.

Let Your fire fall, let Your fire fall.

Lord we've had but a taste of glo-ry, now

Taken from
We Want To See Jesus Lifted High/King Of Heaven
KMCD2438

let   Your fire___ fall.___   Let   Your fire___ fall,_

let   Your fire_____ fall.___

O - pen wide___   the gates___   of hea - ven___   and

let   Your fire_____ fall.____

Let's Bring A Little Heaven

53

Doug Horley

Taken from
We Want To See Jesus Lifted High/King Of Heaven
KMCD2438

the good news__ not just talk__ the good news_____ and if we're
giv-ers and__ not tak - ers we might turn this whole world round. Let's
We can make, we can make,
we can__ make a diff-erence. We can make, we can make a
(Repeat X2)
diff-er-ence to this world. We can make, we can make,
we can make__ a diff-er-ence if we simp-ly start__ to show__ a lit-tle

D.S. al Fine

love to those we know.

2. Each one of us has a part to play in God's plan
   Everyone can be significant
   The key to it all is simply listening to God
   And doing what He tells us.
   Come speak to us, Lord.
   Oh touch us we cry.
   Give us hearts full of compassion,
   Help us reach out in love
   And bring healing to this world,
   As we simply start to show
   A little love to those we know.

Let's Make God Happy

54

Doug Horley

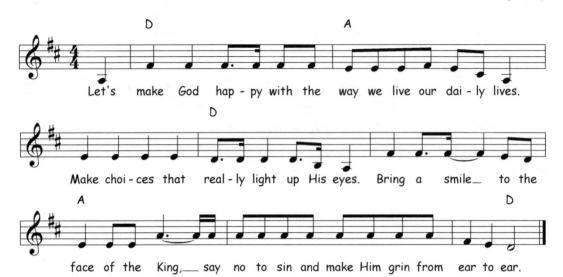

Let's make God hap - py with the way we live our dai - ly lives.

Make choi - ces that real - ly light up His eyes. Bring a smile_ to the

face of the King,_ say no to sin and make Him grin from ear to ear.

Taken from
We Want To See Jesus Lifted High/King Of Heaven
KMCD2438

Lift His Name High

55

Doug Horley

Lift His name high, let the world know, that the
God of cre-a - tion is a - live and well.___ Lift His name
high, let the world know that the way to sal-va - tion, the
hope for our na - tion, is Je - sus and He is a - live.___
Je-sus is the King of glo-ry, this is no fai-ry sto-ry, let the world know
Je - sus is a - live.___ Mend - ing lives hurt and bro - ken,
words of heal - ing spo - ken. Let the world know
Je - sus is a - live._____ Lift His name

Taken from
We Want To See Jesus Lifted High/King Of Heaven
KMCD2438 & On Eagles' Wings KMCD2296

Like The River Needs The Rain

56

Doug Horley & Julie Bond

Taken from
We Want To See Jesus Lifted High/King Of Heaven
KMCD2438

Lord Come Shake This House

57

(I Wanna Build With Gold)

Doug Horley

Taken from
We Want To See Jesus Lifted High/King Of Heaven
KMCD2438

Burn right to the heart of my mo - tives and a-gen-das. Lord come and

shake, shake, shake. Come shake this house.

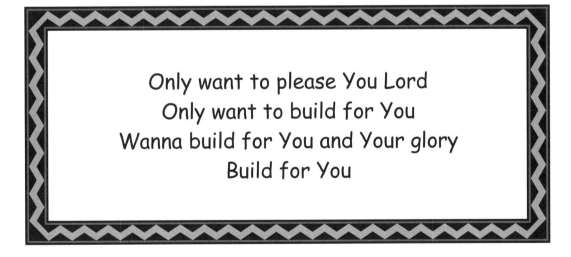

Only want to please You Lord
Only want to build for You
Wanna build for You and Your glory
Build for You

Lovely Jubbly

(He Gave The Mouse Its Squeak)

Doug Horley

Taken from
Lovely Jubbly
KMCD2384

Lord I Lift Your Name On High

Rick Founds

Taken from
Jesus Is The Boss
KMCD827

CMDH05

May Your Love In Me

60

(Let Your Love In Me Light A Flame Within My Heart)

Doug Horley

Taken from
Jesus Is The Boss
KMCD827

May The God Of Hope

61

Doug Horley

May the God of hope— fill you with all joy and peace, as you trust in Him, as you trust in Him. May the God of hope— fill you with all joy and peace, as you trust in Him, as you trust in Him. So that you might o-ver flow— with hope, by the pow-er of the Ho-ly Spi-rit. So that you might o-ver flow— with hope, with hope, by the pow-er of the Ho-ly Spi-rit. May the Fa-ther God, I love You, Fa-ther God I

Taken from
Lovely Jubbly
KMCD2384

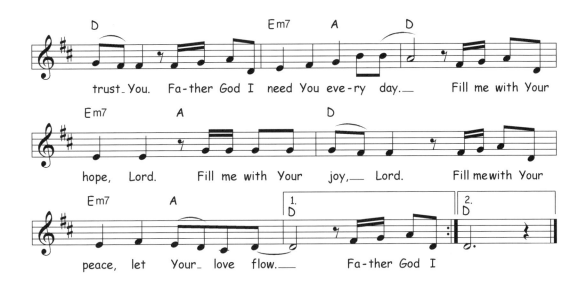

trust You. Fa-ther God I need You eve-ry day.— Fill me with Your

hope, Lord. Fill me with Your joy,— Lord. Fill me with Your

peace, let Your love flow.— Fa-ther God I

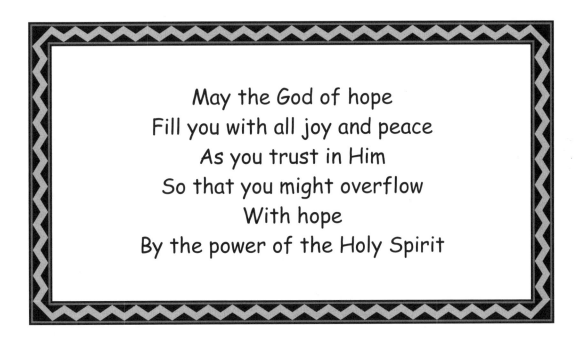

May the God of hope
Fill you with all joy and peace
As you trust in Him
So that you might overflow
With hope
By the power of the Holy Spirit

Noah Was A Faithful Man Of God

62

Doug Horley, Jonathan Roddick
& Pete Bignall

No-ah was a faith-ful man_ of God,_ No-ah was a faith-ful man_ of God._ No-ah was a faith-ful man_ of God,_ _ cos you know he list-ened and o - beyed.____ Put your faith in_ the God who keeps His pro - mi-ses, faith in the one who will keep His_ word._ Put your faith in_ your God, you know you can trust Him. He is the one who saves._ And we will praise Him. We will praise Him for-e-ver. Praise Him, He is Lord of_ all._ We will praise Him, we will praise Him for-e-ver,

Taken from
Okey Dokey
CHMCD034

He is the Lord of all.___ He is the Lord of all.___

He is the Lord of all.___

Put your faith in the God
Who keeps His promises
Faith in the one
Who will keep His word
You know you can trust Him
He is the one who saves

Not Living For My Gain

63

(Free To Live In Your Love)

Doug Horley

Not liv-ing for my___ gain or for ap-plause.___

No room for my glo-ry, but on-ly for

Yours. Wan-na live in Your pre - sence, filled with Your joy.___

Wan-na be, wan-na be, wan-na be set free by the power of Your love.___

Re-lease the e-mo - tion locked up in-side.___ Re-lease in-hi-bi -

tion trapped by fool-ish pride. Wan-na live in Your free -

dom, filled with Your joy.___ Wan-na be, wan-na be, wan-na

be set free by the power of Your love.___ Free to live in Your love,-

Taken from
We Want To See Jesus Lifted High/King Of Heaven
KMCD2438

free   to die   in Your   love.___ Wan-na be,   wan-na be,   wan-na

be set free by the power of Your   love.___   Free to dream in Your   love,_

free   to drown   in Your   love.___ Wan-na be,   wan-na be,   wan-na

be   set   free   by the power   of   Your   love._____

Nothing's Too Big Big Big For His Power

Doug Horley

Taken from
Okey Dokey
CHMCD034

tains,— loves you more than you will ev - er— know,

Oh, oh, oh.— Noth - ing's too Noth - ing's too

big, noth - ing's too small, noth - ing's too

much He cares— for it all. Noth - ing's too all. He is

Now, Now And Ev'ry Day

(Words Are Not Enough)

Doug Horley & Steve Whitehouse

65

Taken from
Fandabidozzie
CHMCD023

Oh It's Great, Great, Brill, Brill

Doug Horley

Taken from
Jesus Is The Boss KMCD827 &
Whoopah Wahey KMCD2217

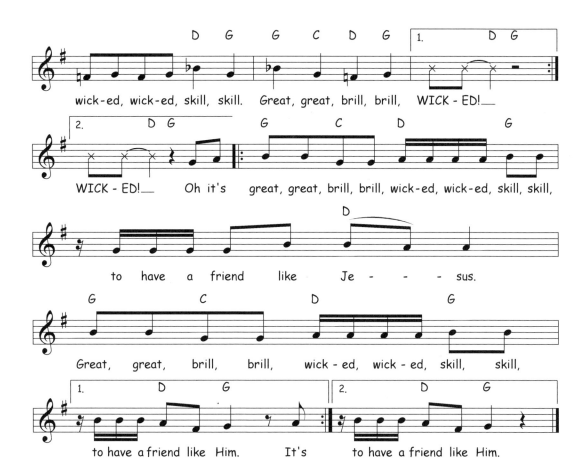

wick-ed, wick-ed, skill, skill. Great, great, brill, brill, WICK - ED!__

WICK - ED!__ Oh it's great, great, brill, brill, wick-ed, wick-ed, skill, skill,

to have a friend like Je - - - sus.

Great, great, brill, brill, wick - ed, wick - ed, skill, skill,

to have a friend like Him. It's to have a friend like Him.

Oi, Oi, We Are Gonna Praise The Lord

Doug Horley

Oi, oi, we are gon-na praise the Lord.__ Oi, oi, we are gon-na praise the Lord.__ Oi, oi, we are gon-na praise the Lord.__ He's an ex-ci-ting, pow-er-is-ing, co-lo-ssal, hu-mun-gous-man-gous God.

It's some-times hard to un-der-stand that the God who made the earth and man would point a fin-ger down from hea-ven and shout, "Hey you! I love you. Hey you! I love you. Hey you! You! I love you", but it's true!

Taken from
We Want To See Jesus Lifted High/King Of Heaven
KMCD2438

On Eagles' Wings

(I'll Carry You On Eagles' Wings)

Doug Horley & Louise Fellingham

I'll car-ry you, on ea-gles' wings.

On ea-gles' wings___ a-cross the sky___ I'll car-ry you.

'Cross moun - tains___ high___ and
I know you're___ hurt,___ I

des - erts dry,___ I'll car-ry you. When
feel your wounds,___ I'll car-ry you. You're

thun - der roars and light-ning strikes, I'll car-ry you.
tired and weak, you've bat - tled hard, I'll car-ry you.

'Cross end - less o - ceans feel my breath, I'll
No power in heaven can shake my strength, I'll

car-ry you. From grey skies cold to blue skies high,
car-ry you. From grey skies cold to blue skies high,

let my breath of life___ car - ry you.___ I'll car-ry
lift your head and come,___ come and fly.___ I'll car-ry

Taken from
On Eagles' Wings
KMCD2296

Okey Dokey

69

Doug Horley
Rap: Efrem Buckle

Taken from
Okey Dokey
CHMCD034

D.C. al Fine

Rap:

Let's jump, let's sing
Our praise to God let's bring
It's time to praise so join our craze
And let the Lord's praise ring
Let's dance, no doubt
Let's praise this party right out
We feel the grace of God in this place
So praise the Lord with a shout
Come on!

Power To Live

70

Doug Horley

Intro:

He's a he not an it, what's that you say?
He's a he not an it, what's that you say?
He's a he not an it, what's that you say?
He's a he not an it, what you talkin' about?

Pow-er to live. Pow-er that's
with us eve - ry - day. That speaks in - to___ our hearts___
_ and says son you are___ O___ K.___ Pow-er to live.
Pow-er to know the Fath - er's___ heart. To
hear the words He cries___ and the strength to speak them out.___
_ Pow - er to live.

Taken from
Jesus Is The Boss
KMCD827

Rap

```
      Gm                    F
He's a he not an it and He is the power of God.
      Gm                        F
Jesus said I've gotta go, but I'll send one from above
          Gm                    F
Who is the comforter, encourager, deliv'rer of men.
Gm                      F
Listen to me now I said again and again.


Gm                    F
Gentle as a dove, yet as strong as a lion
      Gm                  F
Like a mighty rushing wind blowing through mankind.
    Gm            F
His mission is clear, oh there is no doubt
        Gm                      F
He's here on the earth to see the Father's will worked out.


Gm                  F    Gm              F
Worked out baby - yeah - worked out baby - yeah.
Gm                  F    Gm              F
Worked out baby - yeah - worked out baby - yeah.


Gm                          F
You want Him, you've got Him, open up your heart.
Gm                          F
You want Him, you've got Him, open up your heart.
Gm                          F
You want Him, you've got Him, open up your heart.
Gm  F    D
Say, say, yeah.
```

Put Your Hands In The Sky

71

(Will You Get A Bit Funky?)

Doug Horley

(Capo 2 Em)

Fm (Em)

Will you get a bit fun - ky? Will you get a bit frea - ky?

Will you go, go cra-zy to - night? Will you get a bit fun-ky?

Will you get a bit wig - gy, wig - gy? Will you go cra - zy to - night?

%. Fm (Em)   Gm (F#m)

Put your hands in the sky, oh yeah.__ Get

Ab/Bb (G/A)   Fm (Em)

rea-dy to fly,__ ah.____ Put your hands in the sky, oh yeah._

Gm (F#m)   Ab/Bb (G/A)   1.

Get rea - dy__ to__ fly.____ Put your

2. Ab/Bb (G/A)   Fm (Em)

rea - dy__ to__ fly.____ Jump left, jump right,

jump left, jump right, put your hands to - ge - ther ev' - ry -

Taken from
Whoopah Wahey
KMCD2217

Prayin' Is Sayin'

Doug Horley

Prayin'- is say - in' hel - lo to my mate. Prayin' is say - in'

hel - lo to my mate. Prayin' is say - in' hel - lo to my mate.

Whose name, His name. Whose name, His name. Whose name, His name.

Je - - - sus!

Taken from
Jesus Is The Boss
KMCD827

Run The Race

(Every Day I'll Run This Race)

Doug Horley

Eve-ry day I'll run this race, set my eyes u-pon Your face.

Run-ning for the King of kings and the smile of hea-ven.

You are here__ to cheer me on, Your love it will make me strong;

though it may be tough, You know I'll ne-ver, e-ver stop. I'm gon-na

praise You now, come on, come on. I'm gon-na praise You now

come on, come on. I'm gon-na praise You now come on, come on.

Lift your hands up to the sky and let your prais-es fly high.

Lift your hands up to the sky.__

Taken from
Lovely Jubbly
KMCD2384

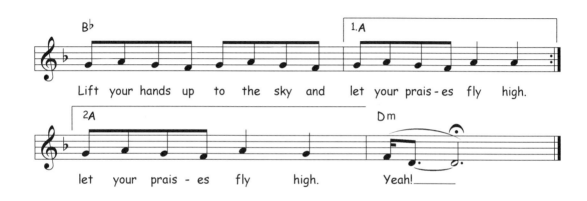

Lift your hands up to the sky and let your prais-es fly high.

let your prais - es fly high. Yeah!_____

Every day I'll run this race
Set my eyes upon Your face
Running for the King of kings
And the smile of heaven
You are here to cheer me on
Your love it will make me strong

Righteousness, Peace, Joy

74

Helena Barrington

Right-eous-ness, peace,_ joy_ in_ the Ho-ly Ghost._

Right-eous-ness, peace and joy_ in_ the Ho-ly Ghost,

that's the King - dom of God._

that's the King - dom of God._ Don't you want to be a

part of His King - dom?_ Don't_ you want to be a part of His King - dom?_

_ Don't you want to be a part of His King - dom?_

Come on ev'-ry-bo - dy._

There is joy in the King - dom,_
There is peace in the King - dom,_
There is love in the King - dom,_

there is joy in the King - dom,_ there is
there is peace in the King - dom,_ there is
there is love in the King - dom,_ there is

Taken from
Jesus Is The Boss
KMCD827

joy in the King - dom.___   Come on ev' - ry-bo - dy.___
peace in the King - dom.___   Come on ev' - ry-bo - dy.___
love in the King - dom.___   Come on ev' - ry-bo - dy.___

that's   the   King   -   dom   of   God.___

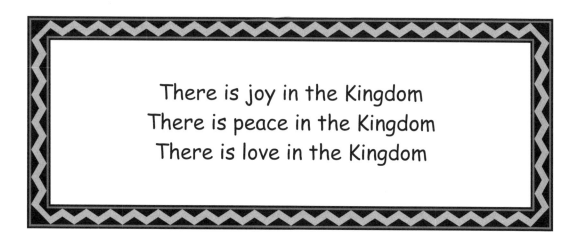

There is joy in the Kingdom
There is peace in the Kingdom
There is love in the Kingdom

Small Is The Gate

75

Doug Horley

Small is the gate and nar-row the road__ that leads to hea-ven.__ Wide is the gate and broad is the road__ that leads to hell. It's not al-ways ea-sy-pea-sy, le-mon squee-zy being a Christ-ian. It's not just a bed of ro-ses, it-'ll keep you on your toes-es eve-ry day.__ The road to hell is ea-sy, just please your-self, be-lieve me, you will find it. The road to life is tough-er, the road to life is rough-er and

Taken from
Lovely Jubbly
KMCD2384

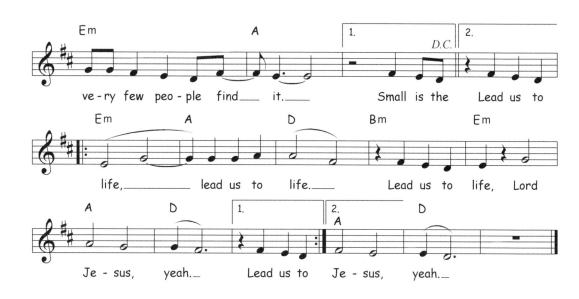

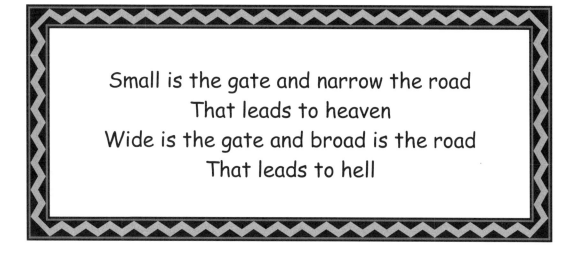

Small is the gate and narrow the road
That leads to heaven
Wide is the gate and broad is the road
That leads to hell

Take It Out

76

Doug Horley & Vanessa Freeman

Take it out to the peo - ple. Take it out to the world.

Take it out to the lost ones. Have you heard?_____

There's a new breeze blow - in'__ now._____ Have you heard?__

Have__ you heard?__

It's time to put your faith in place. Do you walk in

free-dom? It's time__ just to dream a-gain,

list-en to the voice with-in__ us._____ _ It's time to put your

voice with-in__ us._____ Have you heard?_____

Taken from
We Want To See Jesus Lifted High/King Of Heaven
KMCD2438

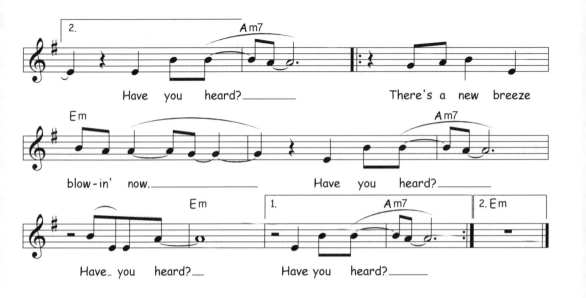

Have you heard?_____ There's a new breeze

blow-in' now._____ Have you heard?_____

Have_ you heard?__ Have you heard?_____

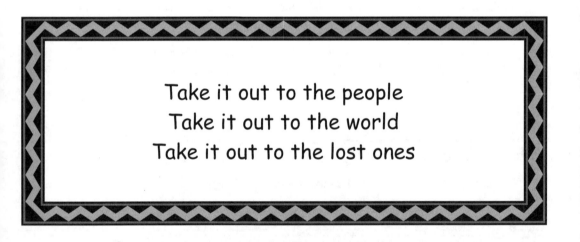

Take it out to the people
Take it out to the world
Take it out to the lost ones

The Funky Skunk

(We Are The Creatures Great And Small)

Doug Horley, Pete Bignall, Jonathan Roddick

Taken from
Fandabidozzie
CHMCD023

out - back's bum-per, jum-per won-der.

We are the crea-tures great and small, us you got-ta love,

made by God a-bove. We are the crea-tures great and small, we've a

great ma-hoo-sive God.

I'm a

shark (shark) with a bad (bad) rep-u-ta-tion.

I come on the scene, peo - ple run and scream. I

don't mean to be rude, but you're not my kind of food. If I

bite your leg in half, I did-n't do it for a laugh. It was a mis -

take, one that an-y-one could make.

us you got-ta love,   made by God a-bove.   We are the crea-tures

great and small. We've a great ma-hoo-sive God.   God.   We've a

great ma-hoo-sive God.   We've a great   ma - hoo - sive

God.

Talk, Talk

Doug Horley

Taken from
Lovely Jubbly
KMCD2384

The Custard Cream Song

(I Love Custard Creams)

Doug Horley

I love cus-tard creams. and Walls ice creams, I love rhu-barb crum-ble and cus-tard. choco-late bars, made by Mars are sim-ply just the best.__ I love in-stant whips,__ sher-bet dips, I love chew-y__ li-quorice all-sorts, but none com-pare to the love that's there in my heart for my friend Je-sus.__ Be-cause__ He loves me,__ be-cause__ He loves me.__ And noth-ing I can e-ver do, or think, or say, or be will e-ver

Taken from
Whoopah Wahey
KMCD2217

The Incredible Song

80

(I Am Incredible)

Doug Horley

Taken from
Okey Dokey

CHMCD034

The Way It's Gonna Be

81

(Capo 2 E)

Doug Horley

Taken from
Fandabidozzie
CHMCD023

The Measure Of The Treasure

(For The Measure Of The Treasure)

82

Doug Horley & Jamie Horley

For the mea - sure of your trea - sure that you store in hea-ven, is the mea-sure that-'ll last for - e - ver.___ But the mea - sure of the trea - sure that you store on earth might be car-ried a-way___ by a thief one day, or rot when the moths get hun - gry.___ For where your trea-sure is,___ that's where your heart_ is.___ For where your trea-sure is,___ there-'ll be your heart.

1. heart.

2. heart.

Taken from
Whoopah Wahey
KMCD2217

The Wobble Song

83

(Everybody Has A Wobble From Time To Time)

Doug Horley

Ev-ery-bo-dy has a wob - ble from time to time.__ Eve-ry-bo-dy has some shake, rat-tle and roll__ in their lives.__ Eve-ry-bo-dy has a wob - ble from time to time.__ Eve-ry-bo-dy has some shake, rat-tle and roll__ in their lives. It's not wrong to have some ques-tions, it's not wrong to have some doubts but some - times we need help from our friends to work things out. To the pro-mi-ses__ He's made us we must learn to hold on tight. 'Cos no way will He leave__ us__ e-ven in the dark-est night.

Taken from
Jesus Is The Boss
KMCD827

There Is A God

Doug & Belinda Horley & Penny Webb

There is a God who knows your name. There is a
God who feels your pain. There is a love
hold-ing out for you, don't fight Him off let Him
love you.___ 'Cos He loves you with___ a pa - ssion,___ an
end - less rag - ing fire.___ From e - ter - ni - ty___ to e - ter -
ni - ty___ you are His heart's_ de - sire,___ and if
you could for___ a mo - ment glimpse_ the huge - ness of___ His
heart you'd see___ how He___ sim - ply

Taken from
We Want To See Jesus Lifted High/King Of Heaven
KMCD2438

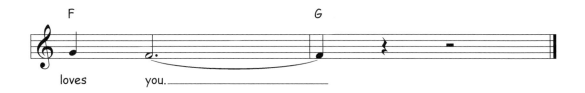

F   G

loves   you.

2. He loves you with a passion, He's always on your side
   Like a mighty wave that won't be stopped.
   His love is ocean wide
   Higher than the heavens above and deeper than the sea
   Truth is, just this, He simply loves you.

3. When you feel you've fallen far too far to ever stand again,
   And you can't believe this Holy God could ever be your friend.
   He's shouting from the heavens above, He's here to help you through
   You'll see, how He, simply loves you,
   Truth is, just this, He simply loves you.

This Is The House Of God

Doug Horley, Vanessa Freeman & Mark Edwards

Taken from
We Want To See Jesus Lifted High/King Of Heaven
KMCD2438

Throw Your Hands Up

86

(Yo, Yo, Whatcha' Gonna Do)

Doug Horley

(Capo 1 Am)

Yo, yo, what-ch'a gon - na do and who - 'ya gon - na be?

Ho, ho, let Him come to you in His hu - ma - ni - ty.

Flow, flow, let His Spi - rit come and let Him fill ya.

Check out the good stuff; He will de - li - ver.

Who was this

man of hea - ven who came down to earth? Who had King

He - rod fright - ened stu - pid when he heard a - bout his birth? Now who on

earth can boast? One of the an - gel host, a - nnounced their i -

mma - cu - late con - cep - tion by the Ho - ly Ghost. But that was

just the start, He was just warm - ing up. He had a par -

Taken from
Fandabidozzie
CHMCD023

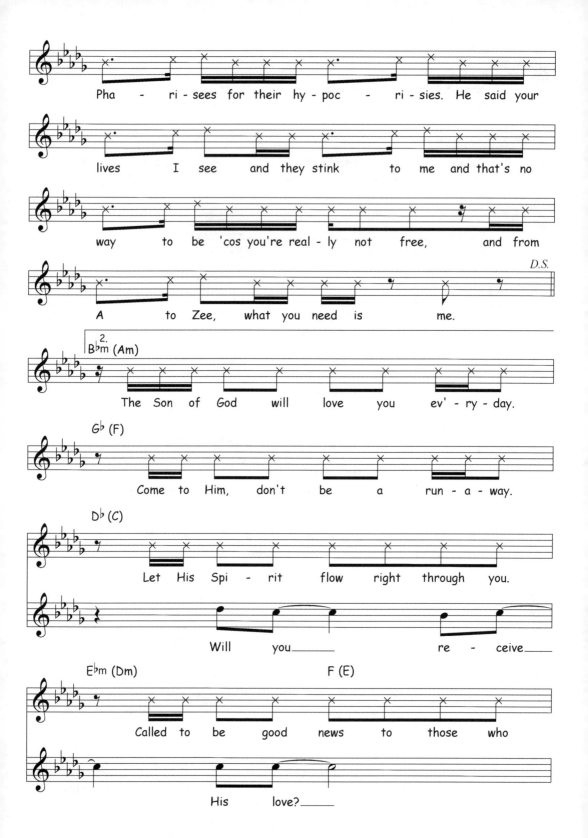

Touch A Finger

87

(Every Bit Of You Is Special)

Doug Horley

Touch a fin - ger,__ touch a thumb,__ touch a wrist,__
Touch a fin - ger,__ touch a thumb,__ touch a wrist,__

touch an el - bow.__ Touch a shoul - der,__ touch a head..
touch an el - bow.__ Touch a shoul - der,__ touch an ear.__

Eve - ry bit__ of you is spe - cial.__ If you're
Eve - ry bit__ of you is spe - cial.__

short and fat or tall and thin, got knob - b - ly knees, or

fif - teen chins. Does-n't mat - ter just what shape you're in, God

loves you as you are. Touch a fin -

ger,__ touch a thumb,__ touch a wrist,__ touch an el -

bow.__ Touch a shoul - der,__ touch an eye -

Taken from
Whoopah Wahey
KMCD2217

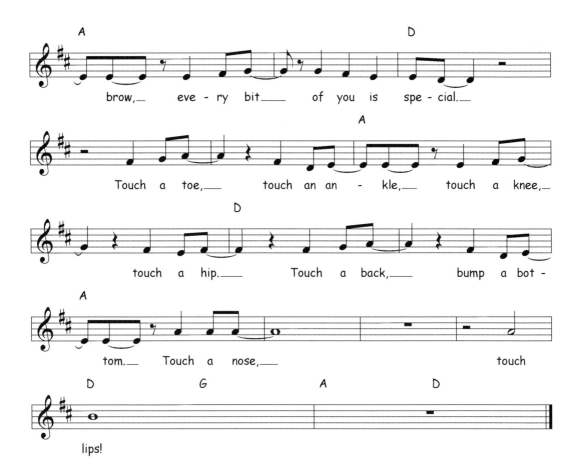

brow,__ eve - ry bit__ of you is spe - cial.__

Touch a toe,__ touch an an - kle,__ touch a knee,__

touch a hip.__ Touch a back,__ bump a bot -

tom.__ Touch a nose,__ touch

lips!

Watch Out!

88

Doug Horley & Mark Read
Rap: Efrem Buckle

Watch out look who's back__ a - gain.
Hold up you can make__ a choice.

Hey you, are you list - en - ing?
Don't think you don't have__ a voice.

Heads up, tell you 'bout__ a friend.
Stand up, start to make__ some noise.

Here goes, are you rea-dy now? He says, you don't have__ to be
Here goes, are you rea-dy now? Shout out, what you wan - na say.

what the world would have__ you be. You can make a stand__ and see
As you live your life__ each day. You can make a stand__ and see

one life mak-ing his-to-ry. So are you one to stand and shout, yeah?
one life mak-ing his-to-ry. So are you one to stand and shout, yeah?

So are you one to get up and dare? Ooh.

Gon-na be a light now, gon-na be bright now just wan-na shine for You.

Taken from
Okey Dokey
CHMCD034

Come on, come on, come on,___ come on yeah.

Put your hands up put them in the air.___

D

Gm

Gon-na be a light now, gon-na be bright now just wan-na shine for You.

Eb **Cm**

World wants to get-cha, I'm gon-na bet-cha. You can hold your head high.

Gm

Gon-na be tough now, gon-na be rough now some will hate your game.

Eb **Cm**

World wants to get-cha, I'm gon-na bet-cha. You can hold your head high.

Gm

Rap:

Yeah put your hands in the air
And wave them with flare
Cos you know God cares
You, don't follow the crowd
You make the Lord proud and darkness back down
Yeah throw your hands in the sky
Wave them real high
All day and all night
You know you can bring the height
As a Jesus Light
Come on and live the life

Waterfall

(In These Last Days The Rains Will Come)

Wayne Drain & Nathan Fancher

Taken from
On Eagles' Wings
KMCD2296

toe   I want it all.____   Hear my   cry,   oh

Lord.   Let the wa - ter   fall.

Wa - ter fall - ing with the   sound__ of a   thou-sand an - gels wings.

Stir - ring heal - ing deep with-in,__   with   ho - nest   hearts.

These songs we'll sing!   Like a wa-ter

We Are Warriors

Doug Horley

We are war-ri-ors,_ gon-na fight and we're gon-na pray.

We are war-ri-ors, gon-na fight and we're gon-na pray.

Kick-in' down the strong-holds of the e-ne-mies of God.

We are gon-na see mi - ra-cles. Cry-ing to our King,

plead-ing for this na-tion, we de - clare we're gon-na break through.

Nat-ter-in', chat-ter-ing, eve-ry day bat-t-lin'

1, 2.
cry-in' out to God we're gon - na break through, break through!

3.
cry-in' out to God we're gon - na break through, break through!

Nat-ter-in', chat-ter-ing, eve-ry day bat-t-lin'.

Taken from
We Want To See Jesus Lifted High/King Of Heaven
KMCD2438

We Have This Treasure In Jars Of Clay

(May We Shine Like)

91

Doug Horley

May we shine like, may we shine like, may we shine like
stars in the dark - ness. stars.
We have this trea - sure in
jars of clay,— for all our frail - ty, You have en-trust-ed us.
To shine your good-ness and life, through-out the na - tions.
We may be pressed hard from ev - er - y side,—
but we will not be crushed, Your hope will streng-then us.
And when the hard times squeeze so tight,—

Taken from
On Eagles' Wings
KMCD2296

may they re - lease more of the fra-grance of Je - sus.

Let Your glo - ry shine.___ Let Your glo - ry shine.___

_ Let Your glo - ry shine,___ through our lives_

_ by Your grace,_ may we o - ver-flow with Je - sus.

We Want To See Jesus Lifted High

Doug Horley

Taken from Jesus Is The Boss KMCD827 &
We Want To See Jesus Lifted High/King Of Heaven
KMCD2438 & On Eagles' Wings KMCD2296

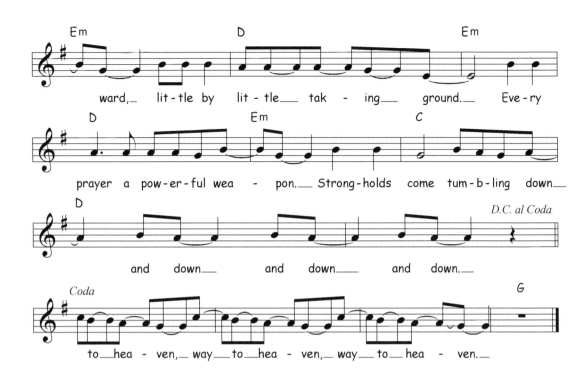

ward,__ lit-tle by lit-tle__ tak - ing__ ground.__ Eve-ry

prayer a pow-er-ful wea - pon.__ Strong-holds come tum-b-ling down__

and down__ and down__ and down.__

to__hea - ven,__ way__to__hea - ven,__ way__ to__hea - ven.__

We're Coming With A New Style

93

Lindz West & Doug Horley

Rap:

We're coming with a new style
Gonna get wild
Gonna make you smile
It'll flip you up turn you upside down
Gonna make you shout flip you inside out
It's the one sure thing that I know here
It's the God sure thing gives me no fear
The cross turned the cost to me from being lost
Now it's time to make him the Boss

Left to right get your hands up
Front to back ev'rybody get your hands up
Tick tock it's time to get your hands up
Yeah... here we go, here we go, here we go... so

Jump to the left ev'ry body with me
Jump to the right for the world to see
Jump to the front then take it right back
Cos Jesus came to save me
Jump, jump to the left ev'rybody with me
Jump, jump to the right for the world to see
Jump, jump to the front then take it right back
What'd he do? He saved me

Verse two, oh, it's on the same tip
Gonna hit you with another rhyme on another trip
With a lesson and a style as we flip this wild
About a man with a plan loves you like His child
So if you're with me and you want it and you wanna get up on it
Then you'd better get on in it in a place deep within it
Cos He's always gonna be there
And He's never gonna leave ya
No, He's never gonna leave you like that

I say, you say, we say Jesus
Jesus rocks! Clap!

Taken from
Okey Dokey
CHMCD034

What Love Is This?

Doug Horley & Steve Whitehouse

What love is this? The love of Je - sus,___ that gave its all, that cost His life. Flesh torn by nails, life cruel - ly ta - ken,___ the Fa - ther's Son, love's sac - ri - fice. And I thank You Lord,___ for lov - ing me and I lift my hands,___ so grate - ful- ly. And I thank You Lord,___ that I can be___ a child of Yours,___ e - tern - al - ly.

You are my
Now let Your

2. You are my King, You are my Saviour.
   You'll always be a friend to me.
   Safe in Your arms now and forever,
   Your light shines bright my morning star.

3. Now let Your power rain down upon me,
   Such peace and joy cascading down.
   May Your love touch all those around me,
   I'll shine for You, I'll shine for You.

Taken from
Lovely Jubbly
KMCD2384

What Greater Gift Has Ever Been Known

Doug Horley

Taken from
Fandabidozzie
CHMCD023

life,   re-jec-ting You for an earth - ly   prize.   How pre-cious

But one day soon,   a - cross the

skies,   You will re - turn   be-fore our   eyes.   And to their

knees   all men will fall,   be-fore their King, our Christ,   our

Lord.   How   pre -   cious

Whoopah, Wahey!

(God Loves Me! Whoopah, Wahey!)

96

Doug Horley

God loves me! Whoo-pah,___ wa-hey!___ God loves you! whoo-pah,___ wa-hey!___ God loves us! Whoo-pah,___ wa-hey!___ God loves you. God loves

I'm gon-na shout, gon-na make some___ noise.___ I'm gon-na sing, gon-na raise my voice. I'm gon-na dance, gon-na go a lit-tle cra-zy. Will you? Will you go? Will you go? I'm gon-na jump, gon-na jump up___ high.___ I'm gon-na raise, my hands___ to the sky.___ I'm gon-na dance, gon-na

Taken from
Whoopah Wahey
KMCD2217

Who's In The House?

97

Carman & Michael A. Taylor

(Rapped)   Born, born, born, born, born.
He was b-born to a virgin named Mary on Christmas Day
He bled and He died on the cross to take sin away.
You take Him high, you take Him low
You take J. C. wherever you go.

Chorus (Rapped)   Tell me who, who, who, who, who?
Tell me who's in the house? - J.C.
Tell me who's in the house? - J.C.
Tell me who's in the house? - J.C.
Tell me who's in the house? - J.C.

Je - sus___ Christ___ is in the house___ to - day.___

The way is straight and nar - row___ and

few there be that find it to - day.___ But there's an

an - gle in the tan - gle and it's Je - sus Christ, He's the way.___

The so - lu - tion to po - llu - tion of the

mind and prob - lems with sin.___ For

Taken from
We Want To See Jesus Lifted High/King Of Heaven
KMCD2438

Dance, dance, we're kickin' it for Christ.
Dance, dance, we're kickin' it for Christ.
Dance, dance, we're kickin' it for Christ.
Dance, dance, we're kickin' it for Christ - Ya'll tell me
Who, who, who, who, who? Tell me

(To Chorus)

Wonderful Lord, wonderful God
You are my shield, my protector
I can lie down, go off to sleep
Knowing You're watching over me

Wonderful Lord

98

Doug Horley

Won-der-ful Lord, won-der-ful God, You are my shield, my pro-tec - tor. I can lie down, go off to sleep, know-ing You're watch-ing o - ver me.__ Won-der-ful Lord, won-der-ful God, help me to trust You for-e - ver. I need not fear, 'cos You are near, I can lie down and sleep in peace.

Taken from
Fandabidozzie
CHMCD023

With Ev'ry Little Part Of Me I Cry

99

(What More Words Are Left To Say?)

Doug Horley & Mark Read

Taken from
Okey Dokey
CHMCD034

You Are A Warrior

100

Doug Horley

You are a war-ri-or,___ a sol-dier of God.___ You have fought ma-ny bat-tles for your King, but now your sword lies___ with your bro-ken_ dreams___ and un-cer-tain-ty's___ a storm whose lash you've felt. You are a war-ri-or,___ a sol-dier of God,___ but each day it's a bat-tle just to pray,___ and there's des-perate need now___ for a fight-er's skill___ and the heart is there but the will is hard to tame. Won't you stand, be-fore_ Him now, lift up your hands and feel___ the po-wer of His love.___

Taken from
Whoopah Wahey
KMCD2217

You Are G.O.D.

101

(Who Would I Really Be)

Doug Horley

Who would I real-ly be,___ if You'd not res-cued me?

I want___ to thank You now___ for - e - ver.

Gave me the gift___ of life,___ gave me the gift___

___ of hope,___ now I am so com-plete in You.___

I wan-na shout it to the sky, shout it to the peo - ple,

shout it to the whole wide world._____ Cos, U R

G. O. D. my God, all the thanks___ I have in my

heart I will give to You. U R G. O. D. my

God, ho - ly, ho - ly one I will wor-ship You now.

Taken from
Okey Dokey
CHMCD034

King of eve-ry-thing. Yeah, yeah, yeah, yeah, yeah.— I will praise You.— Yeah, yeah, yeah, yeah.— Your name— I'll sing. King of the u - ni - verse,— God of my heart. You mean eve - ry - thing— to— me.— Shout it to the sky, shout it to the peo-ple, shout it to the whole wide world.— Cos, King of eve-ry-thing.

D.S. al Coda Coda

You Are Shaped For Serving God

102

(If You Walk Like A Model Or Walk With A Waddle)

Doug Horley & Steve Whitehouse

If you walk like a mo - del or
If you laugh like a don - key or your
If you're good at or - i - ga - mi or can

walk with a wad - dle you are, you are, you're God's
hair's a lit - tle won - ky you are, you are, you're God's
make a great sa - la - mi you are, you are, you're God's

_ in - deed._ If you're ve - ry, ve - ry fun - ny or
_ in - deed._ If you're real - ly good at car - ing or a
_ in - deed._ If you're fast like a whip - pet or

good at mak - ing mo - ney you are, you are, you're God's
lit - tle brave and dar - ing you are, you are, you're God's
real - ly good at cri - cket you are, you are, you're God's

_ in - deed._
_ in - deed._ God had a brill - iant plan when He cre - a - ted man, He
_ in - deed._

knew just how each one would serve Him. Won - der - ful in - deed,

Taken from
Okey Dokey
CHMCD034

You Can Reach Out With A Heart Of Love

103

Doug Horley

You can reach out with a heart of love.
You can reach out with a heart of love.
Make a dif-ference in this world, eve-ry sin-gle boy and
girl take a stand, play a part. No mat-ter how
small you feel, no mat-ter how huge the task,
You can make a dif-ference. Ex-act-ly where you are.
And eve-ry jour-ney starts oh with just one step
and ev-en the great-est life be-gan
with a sin-gle breath. You can reach out with a And when you

Taken from
Okey Dokey
CHMCD034

You Have Captured My Heart

104

(May My Eyes See More Of You Lord)

Doug Horley & Steve Whitehouse

Taken from
On Eagles' Wings
KMCD2296

You Need To Natter To God

105

Doug Horley

Taken from
Jesus Is The Boss
KMCD827

talk, talk, talk - ing___ to the King.___

1.

You need to

2.

You need to nat - ter.___

His heart leaps every time He hears you talking
His heart leaps every time He hears you sing
He's so thrilled when you tell Him
That you love Him

You Won't Get To Heaven On The Back Of A Camel

106

Doug Horley

Taken from
Whoopah Wahey
KMCD2217

You're Worthy Of My Praise

(I Will Worship)

107

David Ruis

I will wor-ship with all of my heart
I will praise You with all of my strength
I will give You all my wor-ship, I will give You
all my praise. You a-lone, I long to wor-ship,
You a-lone are wor-thy of my praise.

Taken from
On Eagles' Wings
KMCD2296

You're A Child Of God

(I Sometimes Feel So Sad)

Doug Horley

I some-times feel so sad,___ 'cos I just can't get things right and ev'-ry lit-tle thing I do___ ends in trou-ble.___ Whe-ther it's wind-ing up___ my mum,- or bit-ing some-one's thumb, I don't want to do it but some-how things just hap-pen.___ And I feel so low that I could be___ a wig-g-ly worm or a ti-ny flea,___ or a snail on a slip-per-y trail,- or a bug in a jug or a yuck-y old slug I feel as worth-less

Taken from
We Want To See Jesus Lifted High/King Of Heaven
KMCD2438

You're The One For Me

Doug Horley & Mark Read

Taken from
Okey Dokey
CHMCD034

Duggie Dug Dug's
Horrible Songs
For
Wonderful Children

Green Thing

(I've Got A Green Thing)

Doug Horley

I've got a green thing— run-ning down my nose. I've got a
green thing— head-ing for my toes.— I need a tis - sue, it's a
real big is - sue, got a green thing— run - ning down
my nose. I've got a green thing—
sit - ting on my fing - er A green thing,— how
long's it gon-na lin-ger? A - long came Bert just to say hel - lo.— We
shook hands once, hey I guess he did-n't know. He had a green thing—
sit - ting on his fin - ger. A green thing,— how
long's it gon - na lin - ger? He bought a sand - wich,

Taken from
Horrible Songs For Wonderful Children
NC201

ate   it   with   re - lish.   Now   there's   no   green   thing   for

an - - y - one   to   che - rish.

Homework, I Hate Homework

Doug Horley

Taken from
Horrible Songs For Wonderful Children
NC201

I'm Suffering With My Wind

112

Doug Horley

Taken from
Horrible Songs For Wonderful Children
NC201

but now my hair has been slight - ly singed.___ I need to

give up my baked bean___ binge, 'cause I'm

B E

suf - fer - ing with my wind.___

Oh Oh My Bald Patch

(I Came Downstairs)

113

Doug Horley

Taken from
Horrible Songs For Wonderful Children
NC201

Plug Hole Song

114

(Why, Oh Why Do I Have To Have A Bath?)

Doug Horley

Why, oh why do I have to have a bath? I don't

want one, I don't need one, it's real-ly not a laugh.

Why, oh why do I have to have a bath? I don't

want one, I don't want one, I don't want one.

Wa-ter in the ri-ver,___ wa-ter in the sea is fine but I don't want

wa-ter o-ver me.___ I'm not e-ven that dir-ty, but my

par-ents get so shir-ty when I say, why do I have to have a

bath? Dirt be-hind___ my ears has

been there now for years___ it's part of me why should it have to go?___

Taken from
Horrible Songs For Wonderful Children
NC201

And I'm real - ly not that smel-ly   and I'd

D.C. al Coda

ra-ther watch the tel-ly.   Oh   why do I have to have a   bath?

Coda

want one.   I don't   want one,   I don't   want one,   I don't

want one.   I don't   want one, I don't want one, I don't   want one.

Sneezing Song

(Put Your Hands Over Your Mouth When You Sneeze)

Doug Horley

Put your hands o-ver your mouth when you sneeze. Put your

hands o-ver your mouth when you sneeze. O-ther-wise a sub-stance

soft and chew-y might land in the face of your friend Hew-y.

Taken from
Horrible Songs For Wonderful Children
NC201

Sunburn Blues

(I Said Ouch! Don't Touch Me)

Doug Horley

Taken from
Horrible Songs For Wonderful Children
NC201

Stop The Car!

Doug Horley

O - oh, I think you'd bet - ter stop the car.

I real - ly don't think we should go too__ far.__

Oh dad, you'd bet - ter hit the brakes quick,__

Oo 'cause I think I'm gon-na be sick! Oops sor-ry,

Oh what the heck! I can see it run-ning down the

back of your neck. But you should wor-ry and curl

your toes.__ What a-bout me? I've got it

run-ning down my nose. In the car the smell will__ ling-er

1997 © Copyright Control
CMDH05

Taken from
Horrible Songs For Wonderful Children
NC201

Oi Josh,— do you want to lick it off your fin - ger?

That plas - tic bag is much too— late,—

'cause we're al - read-y in an aw - ful state.

Index of Titles and First Lines

Songs appear broadly in alphabetical order by author's title. However, in a few instances the strict order has been altered, to allow two-page songs to appear on facing pages. First lines are shown in *italics*.

Duggie Dug Dug Web Site
www.duggiedugdug.co.uk

Includes "Behind-the-scenes" album photos + Harry and Larry games and fun stuff. Plus you'll find lots more information about Doug and his other activities and products. You can order securely online there as well.

Have Doug along to your church!

Doug travels the UK and overseas putting on family Praise Parties, Family Services and training events for children's workers. His concerts are a fast moving and hugely entertaining mixture of puppets, tricks, songs and fun! If you would like Doug to come to your church and do an event for you then please contact him at;

Duggie Dug Dug PO Box 293
Epsom Surrey KT19 9YE UK

Telephone/fax 0208 393 8000
If dialling from abroad +44 208 393 8000

Email duggiedugdug@clara.net